REVISE 11+

Also available to support
Maths 11+ revision:

Maths
Ten-Minute Tests

Series Consultant: Harry Smith
Author: Giles Clare

THE REVISE 11+ SERIES

For the full range of Pearson Revise 11+ titles visit:
www.pearsonschools.co.uk/revise11plus

Contents

How to use this book

Each test corresponds to a practice section in one of the two Revise 11+ Maths Practice Books. The Set 1 tests correspond to the practice sections in Practice Book 1 and the Set 2 tests correspond to the practice sections in Practice Book 2.

Work through the practice sections, then have a go at the matching Ten-minute test.

You could work through the tests in order, or focus on the skills you know you need more practice in first.

Spend 10 minutes on each test and use the answers in the back of the book to mark your work.

1 Ordering and rounding numbers

In this test you will practise using place value to order numbers and to round numbers to a given number of significant figures.

10

1   What is the value of the digit 5 in the number 451 327? Circle the correct answer.

   5   500   5000   50 000   50

1 mark

2   Circle the number with the highest value.

   41 327   42 312   43 212   41 232   43 221   43 122

1 mark

3   Round the number 861 592 to the nearest:

   a   100   _____

   b   10 000   _____

   c   1000   _____

   d   10   _____

4 marks

4   Change the order of the digits in 7176 to make the smallest number possible.

   _____

1 mark

5   Anita completed a number of sponsored swims over five months. She made a table of the distances she swam and the money she raised per month.

Month	Distance in metres	Money raised
January	15 425	£348
February	16 300	£384
March	16 350	£345
April	14 975	£339
May	15 050	£374

   a   Circle the month in which Anita swam the furthest.

   January   February   March   April   May

   b   In which month did Anita raise the least money?

   _____

   c   How far to the nearest 100 m did Anita swim in May?

   _____ m

3 marks

Time to reflect

Mark your test out of 10. How did you do?

Check your answers in the back of the book. If any of your answers are incorrect, go to practice section 1 in Practice Book 1 to revise this topic.

2 Negative numbers

In this test you will practise working with negative numbers in sequences and in data.

1 mark

1 Write the missing number in this sequence.

−11   _____   −3   1   5   9

2 This graph shows the temperature in New York one morning in January.

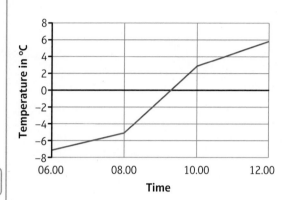

a Circle the temperature at 08.00

     −4 °C   −5 °C   −6 °C   −7 °C   3 °C

b At what time did the temperature reach −6 °C?

_____

c By how much did the temperature rise between 06.00 and 12.00?

3 marks

_____ °C

3 Circle the letter that points to −125

```
←———|———|———|———|———|———|———|———|———|———|———→
   −250   ↑       ↑   ↑       ↑   ↑                250
          A       B   C       D   E
```

1 mark

4 Simone played 6 rounds of golf. Here is her scorecard:

Round	Score
1	−2
2	−5
3	+3
4	+4
5	−7
6	+1

a Write Simone's scores in order, starting with the lowest number.

_____

b In golf, the lowest score is the best. In which round did Simone get her best score?

2 marks

_____

10

Time to reflect

Mark your test out of 7. How did you do?

Check your answers in the back of the book. If any of your answers are incorrect, go to practice section 2 in Practice Book 1 to revise this topic.

2

3 Decimal numbers

In this test you will practise using your knowledge of place value to order and round decimal numbers.

1 Write these numbers in order, starting with the highest value.

| 6.074 | 7.064 | 6.047 | 6.407 | 6.704 |

_____ _____ _____ _____ _____

1 mark

2 Round 9.085 to the nearest hundredth. Circle the correct answer.

9.08   9.09   9.1   9.01   9.18

1 mark

3 Draw lines to match each decimal to the correct rounded whole number.

9.512
0.098
9.053
0.801

9
1
0
10

4 marks

4 Josh is weighing out ingredients for a recipe, but his scales are not accurate. He needs to round the quantities to the nearest tenth of a kilogram. Complete the table.

Ingredient	Recipe weight in kilograms	Rounded weight in kilograms
Flour	1.250	a _____
Butter	0.625	b _____
Sugar	0.305	c _____
Raisins	0.175	d _____

4 marks

5 These are some of the world's fastest times for sprinting 100 m.

Name	Year	Time in seconds
Maurice Greene	1999	9.79
Usain Bolt	2009	9.58
Ato Boldon	1998	9.86
Yohan Blake	2012	9.69

a Write the times in order from slowest to fastest. _____

b In which year was the fastest time recorded? _____

c Harry says, 'You can round both Maurice Greene's time and Ato Boldon's time to 9.8 seconds.'
Is he correct? Circle the correct answer.

yes   no

3 marks

Time to reflect

Mark your test out of 13. How did you do?

Check your answers in the back of the book. If any of your answers are incorrect, go to practice section 3 in Practice Book 1 to revise this topic.

4 Mental addition and subtraction

In this test you will practise using a variety of mental methods to solve calculations and problems. You will also practise using Roman numerals.

10

1 Circle the missing number in this calculation.

 1
mark

4201 + _____ = 8500

4399   4209   4301   4299   4199

2 The Roman Emperor Hadrian was born in LXXVI AD. He died 62 years later.
Write the year he died in Roman numerals.

1
mark

_____

3 A short story competition says entries can be a maximum of 10 000 words long. Suresh has written 9648 words of his story. How many more words can he write before he reaches the limit?

1
mark

_____

4 A bottle contains 1500 ml of water.

a Alicia empties 800 ml of water from the bottle and pours in 150 ml of orange squash.
How much liquid is in the bottle?

_____ ml

b Ewan then drinks some of the squash mixture, leaving 125 ml in the bottle.
How much squash mixture did Ewan drink?

2
marks

_____ ml

5 Which number lies exactly halfway between these two numbers?

969   1031

1
mark

_____

6 For each sequence, circle the amount that is added or subtracted and then write the next term in the sequence.

a 463   412   361   310   _____

    − 49   − 48   − 51   − 50   − 52

b 9491   9701   9911   10 121   _____

2
marks

    + 120   + 220   + 190   + 310   + 210

Time to reflect

Mark your test out of 8. How did you do?

Check your answers in the back of the book. If any of your answers are incorrect, go to practice section 4 in Practice Book 1 to revise this topic.

5 Column addition and subtraction

In this test you will practise using formal written methods to add and subtract whole numbers and decimals.

10

1   Work out the total of 4238 and 3174

_____

1
mark

2   Find the difference between these two numbers.

Eighteen thousand, two hundred and nineteen

Twelve thousand, one hundred and seventy-five

_____

1
mark

3   Riya bakes a selection of cupcakes. She works out how much she spends on ingredients for each box of cakes and how much she sells each box for.

Cupcake	Cost of ingredients	Price per box
Butterscotch delight	£8.56	£12.99
Lemon drizzle	£5.75	£10.50
Strawberries and cream	£6.68	£11.15

a   How much profit does Riya make per box of strawberries and cream cupcakes?

£ _____

b   How much do one box of butterscotch delight cupcakes and one box of lemon drizzle cupcakes cost altogether?

£ _____

c   How much more are the ingredients for a box of butterscotch delight cupcakes than the ingredients for a box of strawberries and cream cupcakes?

3
marks

£ _____

[Test continues on the next page]

5

4 A school kept a record of how many books each class read in a year.
Use this pie chart to answer the following questions.

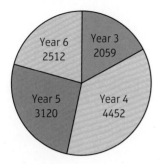

a How many books did Year 3 and Year 4 read altogether?

_____

b How many more books did Year 5 read than Year 6?

_____

c How many books did the classes read in total? Circle the correct answer.

9123   10 431   15 413   12 143   13 431

5 A swimming pool has 29 396 litres of water in it. It needs 7854 litres more to fill it completely.
How much water in total is needed to fill the pool?

_____ l

6 Marisa has saved £14 090 to buy a new car. The car she wants costs £16 500.
How much more does she need to save to be able to buy it?

£ _____

Time to reflect

Mark your test out of 10. How did you do?

Check your answers in the back of the book. If any of your answers are incorrect, go to practice section 5 in Practice Book 1 to revise this topic.

6 Multiplication

In this test you will practise using mental and written methods to multiply whole numbers and decimals.

(10)

1 Raheem thinks of a number. He divides it by 100 and the answer is 98.4
Circle the number Raheem was thinking of.

98 400   9.84   984 000   9840   984

1 mark

2 Complete each calculation.

a $0.4 \times 0.5 =$ _____

b $10 \times$ _____ $= 0.73$

c _____ $\times 1.2 = 1.8$

d $0.8 \times$ _____ $= 6.4$

4 marks

3 What is one thousand, two hundred and thirty-six multiplied by six?

_____

1 mark

4 What is the product of 33 and 41?

_____

1 mark

5 Ashley goes on the same 24 km bike ride 149 times during a year. How far does she cycle altogether?

_____ km

1 mark

6 Circle the multiplication with the lowest product.

1×40 0.1×400 100×0.4 0.01×400 1000×0.04

1 mark

[Test continues on the next page]

7 This bar chart shows the sales of four different items in a stationery shop in January.

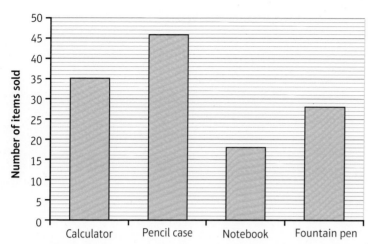

a Notebooks are £4.49 each. What was the total amount spent on notebooks in January?

£ _____

b Fountain pens are £9.32 each. What was the total amount spent on fountain pens in January?

£ _____

c Calculators are £8.84 each. In February, the shop sold twice as many calculators as it did in January. What was the total amount spent on calculators in February?

£ _____

d Pencil cases are £5.68 each. The shop sold half as many pencil cases in February as it did in January. What was the total amount spent on pencil cases in February?

£ _____

7 Division

In this test you will practise using mental and written methods to divide whole numbers and decimals.

1   Complete these divisions.

   a   82 ÷ _____ = 0.82

   b   93.7 ÷ _____ = 9.37

   c   120.3 ÷ _____ = 0.1203

3
marks

2   Circle the correct answer to 58 ÷ 8

   7.10   7.25   7.50   7.80   7.75

1
mark

3   What is three hundred and forty-eight divided by three?

_____

1
mark

4   Olive thinks of a decimal number. She multiplies it by 10 and then by 100, and the answer is 5700
   Circle the number Olive was thinking of.

   5.7   0.57   57.0   0.057   0.0057

1
mark

5   Complete these divisions.

   a   _____ ÷ 11 = 13

   b   69 ÷ 6 = _____

   c   2 ÷ _____ = 0.4

3
marks

6   Amir has collected 129 fossils for a display. Each display case can hold 9 fossils. How many cases does he need to put all of the fossils on display? Circle the correct answer.

   14   13   12   16   15

1
mark

7   Liam has a rope that is 392 cm long. He cuts the rope into 14 equal pieces. How long is each piece?

_____ cm

1
mark

[Test continues on the next page]

8 This table shows the amount of money a group spent on sight-seeing trips on holiday.

Trip	Total cost
Tower view	£442
River cruise	£693
Museum	£375

a 50 people went to the museum.
How much was each ticket?

£ _____

b 25 people went on the tower view trip.
How much was each ticket?

£ _____

c The cost of a ticket for the river cruise was £33
How many people went on the trip?

_____

Time to reflect

Mark your test out of 14. How did you do?

Check your answers in the back of the book. If any of your answers are incorrect, go to practice section 7 in Practice Book 1 to revise this topic.

8 Fractions

In this test you will practise comparing fractions and writing them in different ways.

1 a What fraction of this shape is shaded? Circle the correct answer.

$\frac{8}{10}$ $\frac{6}{20}$ $\frac{6}{10}$ $\frac{4}{10}$ $\frac{3}{6}$

b Write the fraction in its simplest form.

_____

| 2 |
marks

2 Write these fractions in order from smallest to largest.

$\frac{3}{6}$ $\frac{11}{12}$ $\frac{6}{9}$ $\frac{1}{6}$ $\frac{4}{9}$

_____ _____ _____ _____ _____

| 1 |
mark

3 Complete these fractions to make each one equivalent to $\frac{5}{8}$

$\frac{\square}{16}$ $\frac{25}{\square}$ $\frac{\square}{32}$

| 3 |
marks

4 Circle the larger fraction or mixed number in each pair.

a $2\frac{1}{6}$ $\frac{11}{6}$ **b** $3\frac{2}{3}$ $\frac{13}{3}$

| 2 |
marks

5 Here are some number cards.

| 4 | 5 | 9 | 3 |

a Use two cards to write the smallest fraction possible.   _____

b Use two cards to write the largest proper fraction possible.   _____

c Mina says, 'If I use only two cards, the largest improper fraction I can make is equivalent to the whole number 3'. Is she correct? Circle the correct answer.

yes   no

| 3 |
marks

Time to reflect

Mark your test out of 11. How did you do?

Check your answers in the back of the book. If any of your answers are incorrect, go to practice section 8 in Practice Book 1 to revise this topic.

9 Percentages

In this test you will practise comparing percentages and writing percentages in different ways.

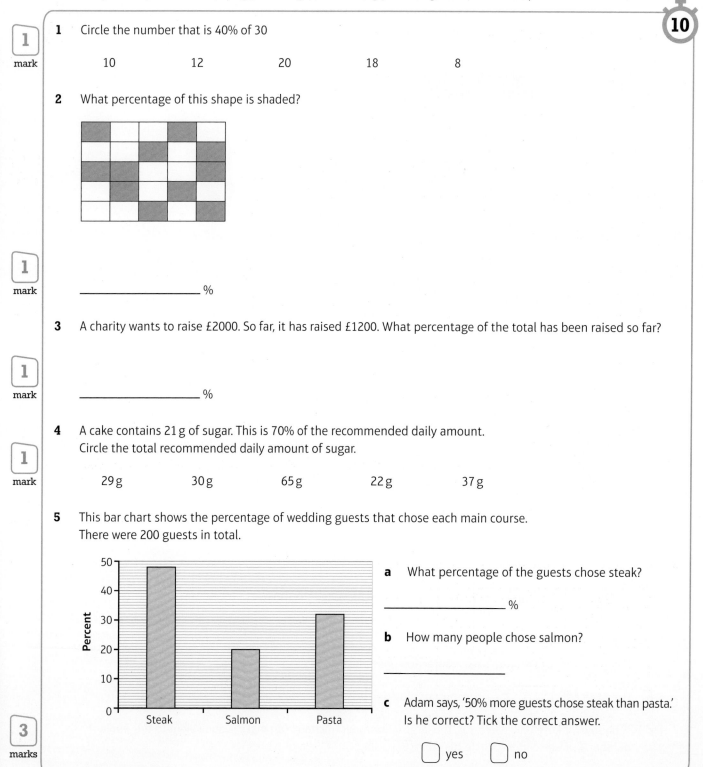

1 mark

1 Circle the number that is 40% of 30

  10   12   20   18   8

2 What percentage of this shape is shaded?

1 mark

_____ %

3 A charity wants to raise £2000. So far, it has raised £1200. What percentage of the total has been raised so far?

1 mark

_____ %

4 A cake contains 21 g of sugar. This is 70% of the recommended daily amount.
Circle the total recommended daily amount of sugar.

1 mark

  29 g   30 g   65 g   22 g   37 g

5 This bar chart shows the percentage of wedding guests that chose each main course.
There were 200 guests in total.

a What percentage of the guests chose steak?

_____ %

b How many people chose salmon?

_____

3 marks

c Adam says, '50% more guests chose steak than pasta.'
Is he correct? Tick the correct answer.

☐ yes   ☐ no

Time to reflect

Mark your test out of 7. How did you do?

Check your answers in the back of the book. If any of your answers are incorrect, go to practice section 9 in Practice Book 1 to revise this topic.

10 Equivalence

In this test you will practise working out equivalent fractions, decimals and percentages.

1 Draw lines to match the equivalent values.

10%
$\frac{1}{4}$
$\frac{2}{5}$
0.6

0.4
$\frac{1}{10}$
$\frac{3}{5}$
25%

4
marks

2 Write these values in order from smallest to largest.

0.76 $\frac{78}{100}$ 75% $\frac{37}{50}$

_____   _____   _____   _____

1
mark

3 Alfie draws a circle with five equal sectors, and colours in one sector.

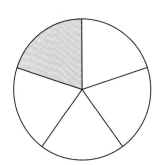

a What percentage of the circle is shaded?

_____ %

b Alfie colours in two more sectors. How much of the circle is now unshaded? Give your answer as a decimal.

_____

2
marks

4 Here are some runners' times from a race.

Name	Time in seconds
Josie	45.1
Mo	43.5
Sara	52.6
Kenzie	56.1
Will	42.7
Rachel	48.9

a What percentage of the runners finished the race in under 46 seconds?

_____ %

b What fraction of the runners finished the race in over 50 seconds?

_____

2
marks

Time to reflect

Mark your test out of 9. How did you do?

Check your answers in the back of the book. If any of your answers are incorrect, go to practice section 10 in Practice Book 1 to revise this topic.

11 Ratio and proportion

In this test you will practise using ratios to solve problems and calculate quantities.

10

1 What is the ratio of shaded to unshaded squares in this shape, in its simplest form?
Circle the correct answer.

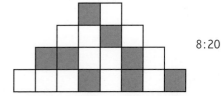

8:20   8:12   2:3   4:6   4:12

1 mark

2 In a dessert, there are 6 strawberries for every 4 blackcurrants. There are 24 blackcurrants.
How many strawberries are there?

_____

1 mark

3 a Sunil and Leo share out 100 football cards. Leo gets 2 cards for every 3 cards Sunil gets.
How many cards does Leo get?

_____

b Sunil and Leo share out a further 120 cards, but this time Leo gets 3 cards for every 2 cards Sunil gets.
How many cards does Leo get this time?

_____

2 marks

4 A recipe for a cake requires these proportions of ingredients:

150 g sugar   75 g butter   500 g flour

Lucy wants to make a cake using 225 g of butter.

a How much flour does she need? Circle the correct answer.

150 g   1000 g   1500 g   450 g   1250 g

b Lucy says, 'I need 425 g of sugar for my cake.' Is she correct? Circle the correct answer.

yes   no

2 marks

5 a Two walls of an octagonal room are painted green, the rest are painted white.
What is the ratio of green walls to white walls in its simplest form?

_____

b Half of the white walls are repainted yellow. What is the ratio of yellow walls to other walls?

_____

2 marks

Time to reflect

Mark your test out of 8. How did you do?

Check your answers in the back of the book. If any of your answers are incorrect, go to practice section 11 in Practice Book 1 to revise this topic.

12 Scale factors

In this test you will practise recognising scale factors and enlarging shapes.

1 A square with 5 cm sides is enlarged by a scale factor of 3
What is the perimeter of the new shape? Circle the correct answer.

20 cm   50 cm   60 cm   45 cm   80 cm

1 mark

2 This diagram shows a parallelogram on a coordinate grid.

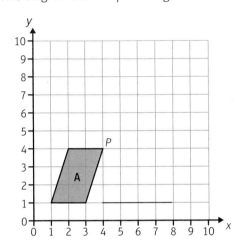

a Enlarge shape **A** using a scale factor of 2
One line has been drawn for you.

b What are the new coordinates of vertex *P*?

_____

2 marks

3 This is a plan for a new housing development on the edge of an existing town. The existing town is a regular hexagon shape and the new housing development is a square.

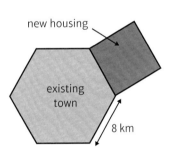

a What is the area of the new housing development?

_____ km²

b The council enlarges the new housing development by a scale factor of 0.5
What is the area of the new housing development now?
Circle the correct answer.

32 km²   64 km²   16 km²   48 km²   144 km²

2 marks

4 This shape has been enlarged by a scale factor of 6

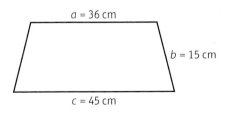

a Circle the original length of side *a*.

6 cm   12 cm   18 cm   3 cm   3.6 cm

b Letitia says, 'Side *c* was originally 7 cm long.' Is she correct?
Circle the correct answer.

yes   no

c What was the original length of side *b*?

_____

3 marks

Time to reflect

Mark your test out of 8. How did you do?

Check your answers in the back of the book. If any of your answers are incorrect, go to practice section 12 in Practice Book 1 to revise this topic.

13 Converting units

In this test you will practise converting and working with equivalent measurements.

10

1 Write these weights in order from smallest to largest.

0.92 kg   920 kg   92 000 g   92 g

1 mark

_____   _____   _____   _____

2 Draw lines to match the equivalent lengths.

200 cm
200 mm
20 m
2 cm

0.2 m
2000 cm
2 m
20 mm

4 marks

3 This bar chart shows the volumes of three different containers.

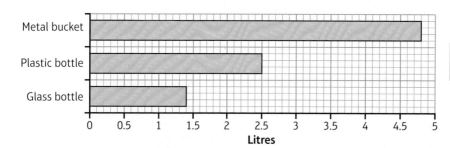

1000 millilitres (ml) = 1 litre (l)
4.5 litres ≈ 1 gallon (gal)

a How much liquid does the bucket hold in millilitres?

_____ ml

b What is the difference in volume between the plastic and the glass bottles in millilitres?

_____ ml

c What is the approximate total volume of all three containers in gallons (gal)? Circle the correct answer.

5 gal   2 gal   10 gal   0.5 gal   4 gal

3 marks

4 Nathan flies 1200 miles to go on holiday to Spain. Work out approximately how many kilometres he flies. Circle the correct answer.

1 mark

800 km   1000 km   500 km   650 km   950 km | 1.6 miles ≈ 1 kilometre (km) |

5 Keira works 35 hours per week. She has 2 weeks' holiday per year. How many hours does she work in a year?

1 mark

_____ | 1 year ≈ 52 weeks |

Time to reflect

Mark your test out of 10. How did you do?

Check your answers in the back of the book. If any of your answers are incorrect, go to practice section 13 in Practice Book 1 to revise this topic.

14 Perimeter

In this test you will practise finding the perimeter of shapes and working out missing measurements.

1   This shape has been drawn on a centimetre-square grid. What is the perimeter of the shape? Circle the correct answer.

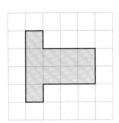

15 cm   17 cm   20 cm   16 cm   18 cm

2   Find the perimeter of this shape.

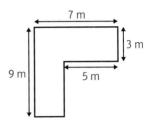

_____ m

3   Swimming pool A is a rectangular shape, 11 m long and 4 m wide. Swimming pool B is also a rectangular shape, 9 m long and 5 m wide.

   a   Which swimming pool has the longest perimeter?

_____

   b   What is the difference between the perimeters of both pools?

_____ m

4   An area of a garden is covered in patio tiles. Each tile measures 50 cm by 30 cm. Here is a plan of the patio area.

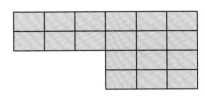

Key

[ ] 30 cm

50 cm

   a   What is the perimeter of the patio area in metres? Circle the correct answer.

        9.6 m   8.4 m   10.2 m   9.8 m   8.0 m

   b   A gardener says, 'If I add six more tiles to complete the rectangle, the perimeter will still be the same.' Is he correct? Circle the correct answer.

        yes   no

[Test continues on the next page]

5 Priya has drawn a symmetrical shape on the playground with chalk. She wants to work out how far it is to walk around the edge of the shape.

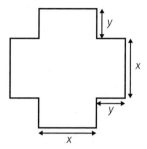

a If x is 100 cm and y is 40 cm, what is the perimeter of the shape in centimetres?

_____ cm

b Priya enlarges the shape so that x is 150 cm and the shape has a perimeter of 1080 cm. What is the new value of y?

_____ cm

2 marks

6 A rectangular field has a perimeter of 1.4 km. The short sides of the field are 200 m long each. How long is one long side in metres? Circle the correct answer.

1 mark

1000 m   200 m   800 m   400 m   500 m

15 Area

In this test you will practise finding the areas of rectangles and using area to work out missing measurements.

1 A square has sides that are 1.1 m long. Circle its area.

10

12.1 m²   4.4 m²   121 m²   1.21 m²   0.44 m²

1 mark

2 What is the difference in area between rectangles A and B?

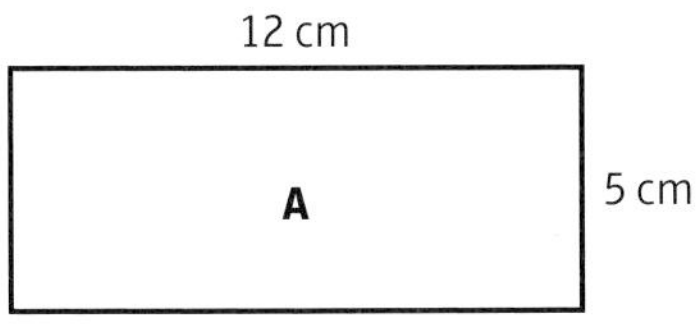

12 cm

A   5 cm

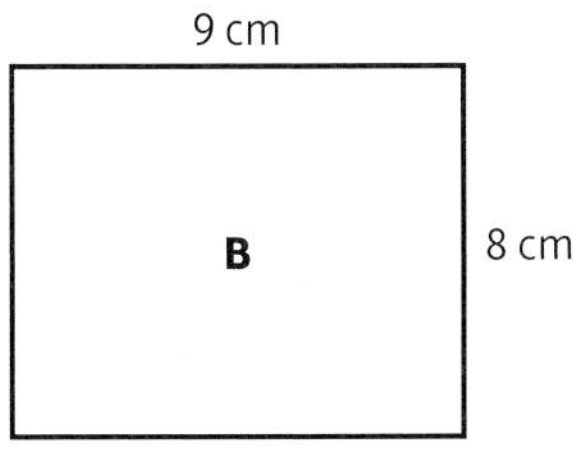

9 cm

B   8 cm

1

_____ cm²

mark

3 A rectangular field is 21 m long. It is 3 times longer than it is wide. What is the area of the field?

_____ m²

1 mark

4 A square has a perimeter of 100 cm. Circle the area of the square.

1 mark

625 cm²   10 000 cm²   6250 cm²   2500 cm²   50 cm²

[Test continues on the next page]

5 This is a plan of Marek's garden.

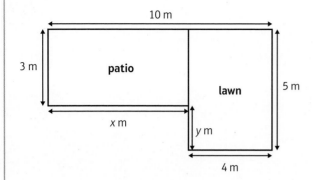

a What is the length of side *x*?

_____ m

b What is the length of side *y*?

_____ m

c Does the patio or the lawn have the largest area?

_____

d What is the total area of the garden?

_____ m²

e Marek decides to replace half of the patio with lawn. What is the new area of the lawn?

_____ m²

16 Reflections and translations

In this test you will practise drawing, reflecting and translating shapes on a coordinate grid.

1 This diagram shows a trapezium.

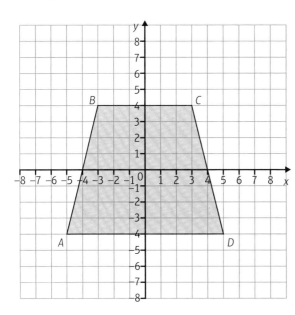

a What are the coordinates of point *A*?

_____

b If the trapezium was translated up 4 and left 1, what would the new coordinates of the following points be?

B _____

D _____

3
marks

2 a Reflect this shape in the *y*-axis.

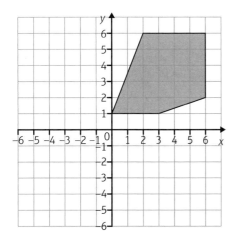

b Now reflect the new shape in the *x*-axis.

2
marks

[Test continues on the next page]

3 This rectangle sits across the *x*-axis. Are the following statements true or false? Circle the correct answer.

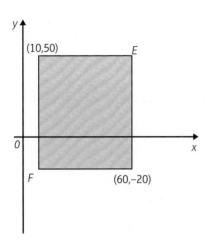

a The coordinates of point *E* are (50, 60).

true   false

b The coordinates (50, −10) are inside the rectangle.

true   false

c If you reflected the shape in the *y*-axis, the coordinates of point *F* would be (−10, 20).

true   false

d If you reflected the shape in the *x*-axis, the coordinates of point *F* would be (10, 20).

true   false

4 The coordinates of the vertices of a triangle are: point *A* (7, 10); point *B* (5, 2); point *C* (9, 2).

a What type of triangle is it? Circle the correct answer.

scalene   equilateral   isosceles

b If the triangle was translated left 7 and up 2, what would the new coordinates of point *A* be?

_____

c The original triangle is translated so that point *B* is at (1, 1). Circle the correct description of this translation.

down 2 and right 3   down 5 and right 2   down 4 and left 2

down 1 and left 4   down 4 and left 1

d If the original triangle was reflected in the *y*-axis, what would the new coordinates of point *C* be?

_____

Time to reflect

Mark your test out of 13. How did you do?

Check your answers in the back of the book. If any of your answers are incorrect, go to practice section 16 in Practice Book 1 to revise this topic.

17 Estimating

In this test you will practise rounding numbers and using rounding to estimate calculations.

1 Complete the table by rounding the numbers.

10

Number	Round to the nearest...	Answer
8239	100	a _____
146 918	10 000	b _____
95	10	c _____
7089	1000	d _____

4
marks

2 a Daniel estimates the total of 454 and 918 to be 1300. Is Daniel correct? Tick **one** box.

☐ yes   ☐ no

b Daniel works out an estimate for a different calculation. He correctly estimates 600
Circle the calculation he is estimating an answer for.

42 × 22   340 + 412   1545 ÷ 3   150 + 650   31 × 19

2
marks

3 A small design company works around the world. Here are its sales figures for one year.

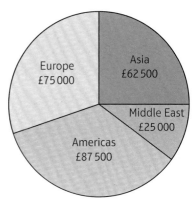

a Round the company's sales in Asia to the nearest £1000

£ _____

b By rounding to the nearest £10 000, estimate how much more money
the company made in the Americas than the Middle East.

£ _____

c By rounding to the nearest £10 000, estimate the company's total sales.

_____

d The sales director of the company estimates that the total sales for two of the regions is £140 000
Which two regions is she looking at?

_____ and _____

4
marks

Time to reflect

Mark your test out of 10. How did you do?

Check your answers in the back of the book. If any of your answers are incorrect, go to practice section 1 in Practice
Book 2 to revise this topic.

18 Multiples and factors

In this test you will practise identifying prime numbers, lowest common multiples and highest common factors of numbers.

10

1 mark

1 Circle the list that contains only prime numbers.

3, 5, 7, 15   2, 3, 7, 12   11, 13, 17, 22   5, 7, 11, 13   7, 11, 14, 17

1 mark

2 What is the total of the lowest common multiple of 4 and 5 and the highest common factor of 10 and 15?

_____

1 mark

3 Circle all the factor pairs of 28

1, 28   2, 14   3, 9   4, 7   5, 6

4 marks

4 Complete the table using the numbers below. Each box may contain more than one number.

84   21   9   14

	Factors of 42	Multiples of 3
Multiples of 7		
Factors of 63		

1 mark

5 Tick the statement that is true.

☐ **A** The lowest common multiple of 6 and 8 is 24

☐ **B** 5 is a prime number and a multiple of 25

☐ **C** The highest common factor of 32 and 48 is 8

6 Use one or more of these number cards to answer these questions.

| 9 | 1 | 2 | 9 |

a What is the closest multiple of 11 to 100?

_____

2 marks

b What is the closest prime number to 20?

_____

Time to reflect

Mark your test out of 10. How did you do?

Check your answers in the back of the book. If any of your answers are incorrect, go to practice section 2 in Practice Book 2 to revise this topic.

19 Order of operations

In this test you will practise working out calculations with brackets and multiple operations in the correct order.

1   Circle the correct answer to $10 + 4^2 \times 2$

52   784   42   74   392

2   Draw one set of brackets in this calculation to make it correct.

21   ÷   3   +   4   ×   6   =   18

3   Circle true or false for each calculation.

a $(3 \times 2)^2 = 3^2$ true   false

b $7 + 28 \div 7 = 11$ true   false

c $41 - 11 + 30 = 0$ true   false

d $10 \times (2 + 1)^3 \div 3 = 90$ true   false

4   Draw lines to match each calculation with the correct answer.

$6 + 3 - 5$
$4 \times 6 - 4^2$
$5^2 - 6 \times 3$
$6 \div 4 \times 6$

7
9
8
4

5   Write =, < or > in the boxes to make each pair of calculations correct.

a $6 + (3 \times 9)$ ☐ $(6 + 3) \times 9$

b $10 \times (2^3 + 2)$ ☐ $(10 \times 2^3) + 2$

c $30 + 5 \times 4$ ☐ $5 \times 4 + 30$

6   Lakshmi has written the following calculation. Is she correct? Circle the correct answer.

$2 \times 2 + 2 \times 2 = 2 + 2 \times 2 + 2$

yes   no

Time to reflect

Mark your test out of 14. How did you do?

Check your answers in the back of the book. If any of your answers are incorrect, go to practice section 3 in Practice Book 2 to revise this topic.

20 Comparing fractions

In this test you will practise comparing and ordering fractions.

10

1 Complete the equivalent fractions.

a $\frac{8}{3} = \frac{\square}{9}$

b $\frac{36}{20} = \frac{9}{\square}$

c $2\frac{4}{6} = \frac{\square}{6}$

d $1\frac{3}{5} = \frac{16}{\square}$

e Which two of your answers are equivalent to each other? Write the letters.

_____ and _____

5 marks

2 Circle the equivalent value for $\frac{10}{8}$

$\frac{6}{4}$ $1\frac{3}{4}$ $1\frac{1}{4}$ $\frac{8}{5}$ $\frac{6}{5}$

1 mark

3 Circle the smaller value in each pair.

a $3\frac{1}{3}$ $\frac{39}{12}$

b $\frac{99}{15}$ $\frac{32}{5}$

2 marks

4 Write <, > or = between each pair of values to make a true statement.

a $\frac{2}{5}$ $\square$ $\frac{1}{4}$

b $1\frac{3}{5}$ $\square$ $1\frac{2}{3}$

c $\frac{30}{8}$ $\square$ $3\frac{3}{4}$

3 marks

5 Look at these fractions.

$\frac{27}{36}$ $\frac{15}{12}$ $\frac{8}{7}$ $\frac{4}{3}$ $\frac{10}{15}$

a Which fraction is the largest? _____

b Which fraction is the smallest? _____

3 marks

c Which fraction is closest to 1? _____

Time to reflect

Mark your test out of 14. How did you do?

Check your answers in the back of the book. If any of your answers are incorrect, go to practice section 4 in Practice Book 2 to revise this topic.

21 Calculating with fractions

In this test you will practise adding, subtracting, multiplying and dividing fractions.

1 Circle the correct answer to $\frac{5}{6} - \frac{1}{3}$

$\frac{2}{6}$ $\qquad$ $\frac{2}{3}$ $\qquad$ $\frac{1}{3}$ $\qquad$ $\frac{1}{2}$ $\qquad$ $\frac{1}{4}$

2 Write <, > or = in the boxes between each pair of calculations to make a true statement.

a $\frac{6}{8} + \frac{1}{4}$ ☐ $1\frac{1}{4} - \frac{2}{6}$ $\qquad\qquad$ **b** $\frac{2}{3} \times 9$ ☐ $3 \div \frac{1}{2}$

c $\frac{5}{7} \times 3$ ☐ $3\frac{1}{7} - \frac{6}{7}$

3 marks

3 A fruit salad contains 4 types of fruit: apple, banana, grapes and melon.
There are 240 pieces of fruit altogether. $\frac{1}{3}$ of the fruit is apple and $\frac{1}{4}$ is banana.

a How many pieces of apple are there?

_____

b Work out the total number of grapes and pieces of melon in the fruit salad.

_____

2 marks

4 This pie chart shows the favourite colours of 360 children. 30 children chose purple.

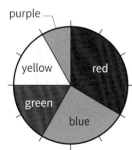

a How many children chose green as their favourite colour?

_____

b What fraction of the children chose red, blue or purple as their favourite colour? Write your answer in its simplest form.

_____

c How many more children chose red than blue as their favourite colour?

_____

3 marks

5 Danny has $3\frac{3}{4}$ bars of chocolate. He shares it between 3 of his friends.

a How much chocolate did each person get? Write your answer as a fraction of chocolate bars.

_____

b Each bar contains eight pieces of chocolate. How many pieces of chocolate does each person get?

_____

2 marks

Time to reflect

Mark your test out of 11. How did you do?

Check your answers in the back of the book. If any of your answers are incorrect, go to practice section 5 in Practice Book 2 to revise this topic.

22 Areas of other shapes

In this test you will practise finding the areas of parallelograms, triangles and combinations of shapes.

(10)

1 | 1   Circle the area of a parallelogram with a base of 4.8 cm and a height of 5 cm.
mark

     12 cm²   32 cm²   26 cm²   30 cm²   24 cm²

1 | 2   A triangle has an area of 112 m² and a base of 16 m. What is its height?
mark

_____ m

3   Omar draws a parallelogram like this.

6 cm

5 cm

   What will the new area of the parallelogram be if he enlarges it by a scale factor of 0.5?

1 |
mark   _____ cm²

4   What is the difference in area between these triangles? Circle the correct answer.

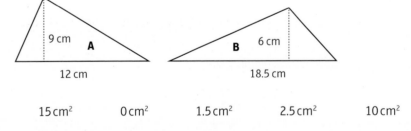

9 cm   **A**

12 cm

B   6 cm

18.5 cm

1 |
mark   15 cm²   0 cm²   1.5 cm²   2.5 cm²   10 cm²

5   This shape is made from two identical parallelograms and a triangle. The shaded parallelogram in this shape has an area of 40 cm². What is the area of triangle **A**?

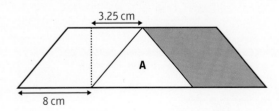

3.25 cm

A

8 cm

1 |
mark   _____ cm²

[Test continues on the next page]

6 Here is a tent.

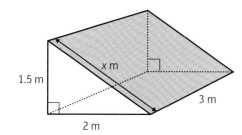

1.5 m

x m

3 m

2 m

a The area of the shaded side is 7.5 m². How long is side *x*?

_____ m

b What is the area of the base of the tent?

_____ m²

c The tent manufacturer buys 1050 m² of material. The material is used on all 5 faces of the tent. How many tents can she make in total?

_____

3 marks

Time to reflect

Mark your test out of 8. How did you do?

Check your answers in the back of the book. If any of your answers are incorrect, go to practice section 6 in Practice Book 2 to revise this topic.

23 Volume

In this test you will practise finding the volume of cubes, cuboids and 3D shapes made from cubes.

10

1 This shape is made from cubes with sides of 1 cm. Circle the volume of this shape.

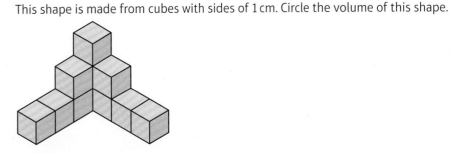

1 mark

　7 cm³　　　11 cm³　　　10 cm³　　　8 cm³　　　12 cm³

2 Shauna makes a cuboid using 1 cm³ cubes. It is 2 cubes wide, 7 cubes long and 6 cubes tall. Shauna breaks her cuboid into two pieces. One of them is shown in the diagram.
What is the volume of the other piece of the cuboid?

1 mark

_____ cm³

3 What is the volume of a cuboid with sides of 110 mm, 70 mm and 100 mm?

1 mark

_____ mm³

4 A cuboid has a height of 6 cm, a width of 3 cm and a volume of 90 cm³. What is its length?

1 mark

_____ cm

[Test continues on the next page]

5 The length of each side of a cube is halved. How many times smaller is its new volume than its original volume?

$\boxed{1}$ mark

8 times   2 times   3 times   10 times   5 times

6 Here is a cuboid-shaped cake.

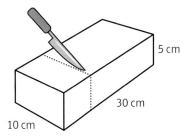

5 cm

30 cm

10 cm

a What is the volume of the whole cake?

_____ cm³

b The cake is cut into two pieces as shown, so that one person gets twice as much as another person. Circle the volume of the smaller piece of cake.

250 cm³   1000 cm³   750 cm³   1500 cm³   500 cm³

c The larger piece of cake is then cut in half parallel to the original cut. What are the dimensions of each of the three new pieces?

_____ cm   _____ cm   _____ cm

d How many whole cakes could you fit in a box measuring 1 m wide, 1.2 m long and 1 m tall?

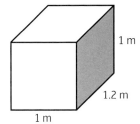

1 m

1.2 m

1 m

$\boxed{4}$ marks

_____

Time to reflect

Mark your test out of 9. How did you do?

Check your answers in the back of the book. If any of your answers are incorrect, go to practice section 7 in Practice Book 2 to revise this topic.

24 Square and cube numbers

In this test you will practise identifying square and cube numbers, and calculating with them.

(10)

1 mark

1 Circle the number that is equal to 80^2

    64   800   8000   6400   640

1 mark

2 Write down the missing number in this sequence.

    27   64   _____   216   343

3 **a** Work out $4^2 + 7^2$

    _____

    b Work out $6^3 - 10^2$

    _____

3 marks

    c Work out 8^3 doubled.

    _____

1 mark

4 Write down two cube numbers to complete this calculation.

    _____ − _____ = 56

5 Write =, < or > in the boxes between each pair of numbers to make a true statement.

    a 5^3 ☐ 12^2

    b 3^3 ☐ 5^2

3 marks

    c 8^2 ☐ 4^3

6 Write these square and cube numbers in order from smallest to largest.

    10^3 7^2 5^3 11^2 4^3

1 mark

    _____   _____   _____   _____   _____

Time to reflect

Mark your test out of 10. How did you do?

Check your answers in the back of the book. If any of your answers are incorrect, go to practice section 8 in Practice Book 2 to revise this topic.

25 Triangles and quadrilaterals

In this test you will practise identifying different triangles and quadrilaterals, and understanding their properties.

10

1   How many equilateral triangles would fit into the trapezium? Circle the correct number.

5 cm

15 cm

20 cm

5   6   8   7   9

1 mark

2   What is the size of angle x in this parallelogram?

78°   102°

x

_____°

1 mark

3   **a**   Rhiannon says, 'This quadrilateral has two pairs of equal adjacent sides and one pair of opposite equal angles.' What shape is she describing?

_____

b   Aysha says, 'A scalene triangle has no equal sides and at least two obtuse interior angles.' Is her description correct? Circle the correct answer.

yes   no

2 marks

4   Draw lines to match each shape to the correct name.

trapezium

kite

rhombus

3 marks

[Test continues on the next page]

33

5 Complete the table.

Polygon	Number of equal sides	Number of equal angles
Equilateral triangle	3	**a** _____
Rhombus	**b** _____	2 pairs of equal opposite angles
c _____	4	4 equal right angles

6 The base of a rectangle is drawn using the coordinates (–3, –3) and (3, –3). The rectangle is 7 units tall. What are the coordinates of the other vertices?

_____   _____

7 A trapezium is divided by a dotted line like this.

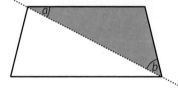

a What type of triangle is shaded?

_____

b Rhys says, 'Angles *a* and *b* are equal because they are opposite.' Is he correct?
Circle the correct answer.

yes   no

c Kwame says, 'The shaded and the unshaded shapes have the same area because the trapezium has been cut in half.' Is he correct? Circle the correct answer.

yes   no

Time to reflect

Mark your test out of 15. How did you do?

Check your answers in the back of the book. If any of your answers are incorrect, go to practice section 9 in Practice Book 2 to revise this topic.

26 Polygons and 3D shapes

In this test you will practise identifying 2D and 3D shapes, and understanding their properties.

1 Draw lines to match each polygon to the correct number of sides.

pentagon		7
hexagon		8
heptagon		6
octagon		5

10

4 marks

2 Identify all the different shapes in each of these patterns.

a _____

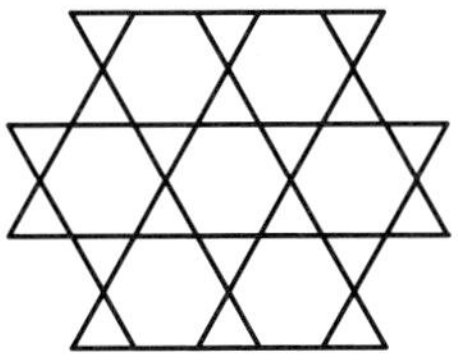

_____

b _____

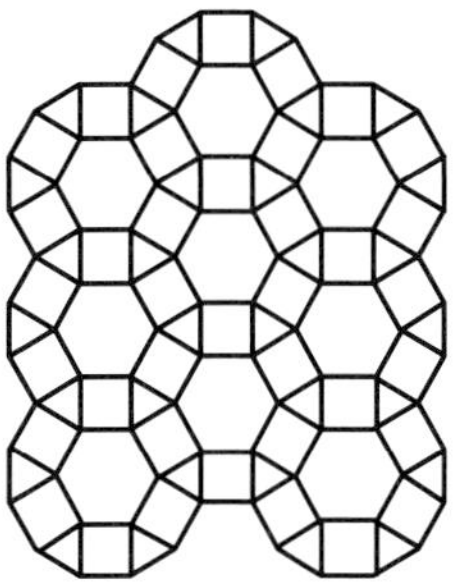

_____

_____

c _____

_____

3 marks

3 Draw lines to match each 3D shape to the correct name.

A   B    C 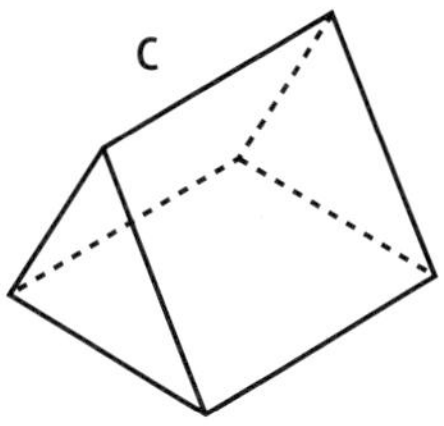   D

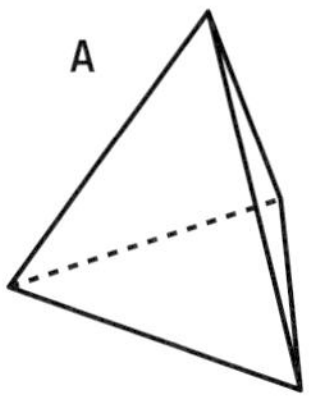

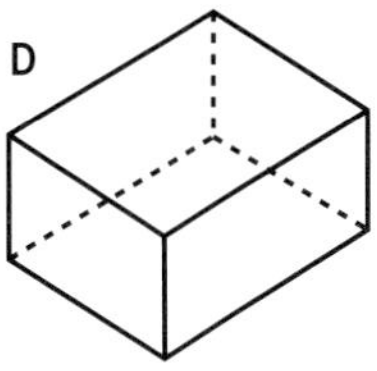

cuboid   triangular prism   cylinder   triangle-based pyramid

4 marks

4 Robyn says, 'This 3D shape has 5 faces, 8 edges and 5 vertices.' What shape is she describing?

_____

1 mark

[Test continues on the next page]

5 What is the name of this polygon?

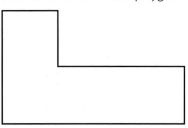

_____

6 Evan draws a polygon on a coordinate grid. He asks, 'What overall shape would be created if I reflected this shape on the *y*-axis?' Write the name of the shape that would be created.

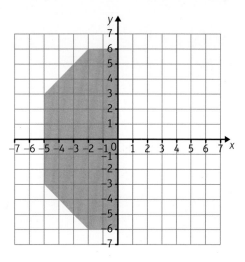

_____

7 Complete this table.

Shape	Number of faces	Number of edges	Number of vertices
cube	a _____	12	8
hexagonal prism	8	18	b _____
cone	2	c _____	1

Time to reflect

Mark your test out of 17. How did you do?

Check your answers in the back of the book. If any of your answers are incorrect, go to practice section 10 in Practice Book 2 to revise this topic.

27 Angles

In this test you will practise naming, estimating and comparing angles.

1 Circle true or false for each statement about this angle.

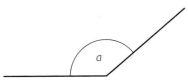

a Angle *a* is greater than 180°   true   false

b Angle *a* is an obtuse angle.   true   false

c Angle *a* is less than 90°   true   false

d Angle *a* is a reflex angle.   true   false

4 marks

2 Circle the correct estimate for the size of angle *b*.

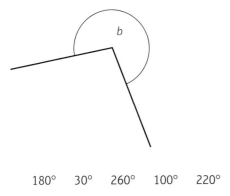

180°   30°   260°   100°   220°

1 mark

3 Draw lines to match each angle size to the correct type of angle.

96°
330°
31°
180°

acute
straight line
obtuse
reflex

4 marks

4 **a** Shannon draws a shape. She says, 'On the inside, it has two right angles, one acute angle and one obtuse angle. It is a trapezium.' Can she be correct? Circle the correct answer.

yes   no

b Shannon draws another shape. She says, 'On the inside, it has one right angle, two reflex angles and one acute angle. It is a kite.' Can she be correct? Circle the correct answer.

yes   no

2 marks

[Test continues on the next page]

5 For each angle, circle the correct estimate of its size and write what type of angle it is.

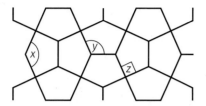

a Angle *x*

95° 200° 230° 180° 130°

Type: _____

b Angle *y*

90° 115° 245° 80° 180°

Type: _____

c Angle *z*

180° 120° 90° 360° 45°

Type: _____

3 marks

6 Circle true or false for each of these statements.

a Angles inside a triangle cannot be reflex.   true   false

b A right angle measures 100°   true   false

c An obtuse angle is smaller than a right angle.   true   false

3 marks

Time to reflect

Mark your test out of 17. How did you do?

Check your answers in the back of the book. If any of your answers are incorrect, go to practice section 11 in Practice Book 2 to revise this topic.

28 Angle properties

In the test you will need to use your knowledge of angle properties to find the missing angles.

1   Look at angles *a*, *b* and *c*.

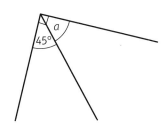 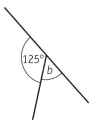 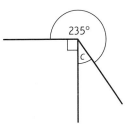

   a   Which angle is the smallest?

   _____

   b   Which angle is the largest?

   _____

   c   What is the size of angle *a*?

   _____ °

3 marks

2   Circle the sum of all four angles in this shape.

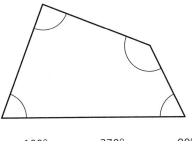

   180°   270°   90°   360°   540°

1 mark

3   Circle true or false for each statement about this parallelogram.

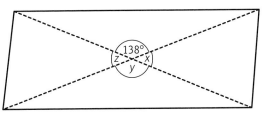

   a   Angle *x* is an acute angle.   true   false

   b   Angle *y* is 138°   true   false

   c   Angle *x* is 52°   true   false

   d $z = 360 - (138 + x + y)$ true   false

4 marks

[Test continues on the next page]

39

4 Work out the size of the missing angles.

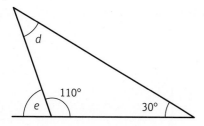

a Angle d _____ °

b Angle e _____ °

2
marks

5 An isosceles triangle has an angle of 92°. What is the size of the other two angles?

1
mark

_____ °

6 Work out the value of f.

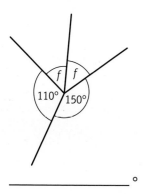

1
mark

_____ °

7 Circle the sizes of the angles marked with letters.

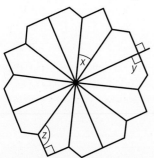

a Angle x   60°   45°   120°   30°   90°

b Angle y   90°   180°   45°   270°   60°

3
marks

c Angle z   200°   90°   120°   180°   150°

Time to reflect

Mark your test out of 15. How did you do?

Check your answers in the back of the book. If any of your answers are incorrect, go to practice section 12 in Practice Book 2 to revise this topic.

29 Equations and formulae

In this test you will practise writing expressions and using formulae to work out values.

1 A loaf of bread with 20 slices costs *x* pence. Circle the expression that shows how much each slice costs.

20*x*   200 − *x*   *x* ÷ 200   200*x*   *x* ÷ 20

1
mark

2 Scott rolls five dice. Two dice land on *a*, one lands on *b* and two land on *c*. The total is 21

a	a	b	c	c

    a Write a formula that expresses this total.

    _____

    b *a*, *b* and *c* are all different whole numbers between 1 and 6. If *a* = 5, what are the values of *b* and *c*?

    b = _____   *c* = _____

2
marks

3 Solve $3d ÷ 4 = 9$

_____

1
mark

4 Using the formula $(3z + 2) × y = 44$, work out the value of *z* when *y* = 4

_____

1
mark

5 A rectangle is twice as long (*l*) as it is wide (*w*). Write a formula for the perimeter, *P*, in terms of width (*w*) only.

_____

1
mark

6 Solve $2x + 25 = 17$

_____

1
mark

Time to reflect

Mark your test out of 7. How did you do?

Check your answers in the back of the book. If any of your answers are incorrect, go to practice section 13 in Practice Book 2 to revise this topic.

30 Linear sequences

In this test you will practise identifying rules and finding missing numbers or the nth term in sequences.

10

1 **a** Circle the linear sequence.

4, 7, 11, 16, 22…   6, 2, −2, −6, −12…   2, 3, 5, 8, 13…

10, 17, 24, 31, 39…   6, 10, 14, 18, 22…

b Circle the correct expression for the nth term of the linear sequence above.

2 marks

$5n − 1$ $4n + 2$ $4n + 1$ $6n − 2$ $5n + 1$

2 Circle true or false for each statement.

6, 15, _____ , 33, 42, 51

a The sequence is linear.   true   false

b The missing term is 26   true   false

3 marks

c The expression for the nth term is $9n − 3$ true   false

3 The expression for the nth term of this sequence is $8n − 2$

6, _____ , 22, 30, _____ …

a Write in the two missing terms in the sequence.

b What is the 11th term in the sequence?

2 marks

_____

4 Write the next three terms of a sequence that has a first term of 105 and a term-to-term rule of 'subtract 9'

1 mark

_____

5 The expression for the nth term of a sequence of numbers is $−3n + 7$
Circle the number that is not in the sequence.

1 mark

4   −2   −5   −1   −8

6 Here are expressions for the nth terms of two sequences.

$6n + 8$ $−6n − 4$

Circle the difference between the 12th term of the first sequence and the 6th term of the second sequence.

1 mark

40   160   60   100   120

Time to reflect

Mark your test out of 10. How did you do?

Check your answers in the back of the book. If any of your answers are incorrect, go to practice section 14 in Practice Book 2 to revise this topic.

31 Tables, charts and graphs

In this test you will practise interpreting data in different types of tables, charts and timetables.

1 Here is a pie chart showing where 400 children went on holiday.

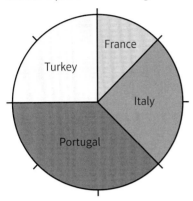

a Circle how many children visited Italy.

200   100   50   150   25

b What fraction of the children visited France?

_____

c Circle the percentage of children that visited Portugal.

35%   25%   12.5%   37.5%   0%

d Circle true or false for each statement.

Italy was more popular than Turkey.	true false
150 children went to Portugal.	true false
Three times more children went to Italy or Portugal than to France.	true false

6 marks

2 Here is a timetable for the trains between Penzance and Bristol. Each train travels at the same speed.

Penzance	09.03	10.45	11.17	12.08
Plymouth	10.59	12.39	13.11	14.02
Exeter	11.56	13.38	14.10	15.01
Bristol	13.02	14.44	15.16	

a Circle the total journey time from Penzance to Bristol.

4 h 1 min   3 h 56 min   4 h 59 min   3 h 57 min   3 h 59 min

b Eva needs to be in Exeter for a meeting at 3.00 pm. What time is the latest train she can catch from Penzance?

_____

c Nikos catches the 12.08 train from Penzance to Bristol. He notices that the arrival time in Bristol is missing from the timetable. What time will he arrive?

_____

3 marks

[Test continues on the next page]

3 This line graph shows a journey Lenny made by bicycle.

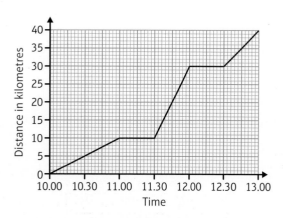

a How many times did Lenny stop for a break on his journey?

_____

b How long did Lenny's journey take altogether?

_____

c Circle Lenny's speed between 10.00 and 11.00

10 km per hour   5 km per hour   2 km per hour   20 km per hour   40 km per hour

d Between which times did Lenny cycle the fastest?

_____

marks

Time to reflect

Mark your test out of 13. How did you do?

Check your answers in the back of the book. If any of your answers are incorrect, go to practice section 15 in Practice Book 2 to revise this topic.

32 Mean average

In this test you will practise working out means and finding missing numbers from means.

1 Work out the mean of these numbers:

1.5, $\frac{1}{2}$, 1.75, $\frac{1}{4}$, $\frac{5}{10}$

_____

2 Jonny used an app on his phone to see how much pocket money he earned and spent each month.

Month	Earned	Spent
January	£21	£12
February	£35	£30
March	£14	£27
April	£11	£13
May	£30	£19
June	£21	data missing

Month	Earned	Spent
July	£24	£20
August	£40	£30
September	£32	£44
October	data missing	£9
November	£19	£17
December	£25	£6

a Circle the mean pocket money Jonny earned in the first half of the year.

£20   £22   £21   £25   £24

b Jonny's average spending in the first half of the year was £18 per month. How much did he spend in June?

£ _____

c How much more per month did Jonny spend on average in the second half of the year compared to the first?

£ _____ per month

d In the last 3 months of the year, the mean pocket money Jonny earned was £25 per month. How much did he earn in October?

£ _____

[Test continues on the next page]

3 Sarah is on a train journey. For the first 3 hours of her journey she travels 80 km per hour. Over the final 3 hours she travels 30 km per hour. Circle Sarah's average speed over the whole journey.

1 mark

40 km per hour   60 km per hour   45 km per hour   50 km per hour   55 km per hour

4 Circle the line of three horizontal, vertical or diagonal numbers with the greatest mean.

1	6	4
9	2	8
7	3	5

1 mark

5 Gemma buys a pack of 20 colouring pens costing £8.00. How much does Gemma pay per pen on average?

1 mark

_____ p

Time to reflect

Mark your test out of 8. How did you do?

Check your answers in the back of the book. If any of your answers are incorrect, go to practice section 16 in Practice Book 2 to revise this topic.

Glossary

| Angle | the point where two straight lines meet |

Acute angle	less than 90°
Obtuse angle	between 90° and 180°
Reflex angle	between 180° and 360°
Right angle	90°
Straight line	180°
Full turn	360°

Area	a measurement of the space covered by a two-dimensional shape
Coordinates	two numbers, in brackets and separated by a comma, that identify the position of a point on a coordinate grid. The first number tells you how far along the x-axis and the second number tells you how far along the y-axis the point can be found
Cube number	the result of multiplying a number by itself twice
Edge	a line where two faces meet on a three-dimensional shape
Equivalent fractions	fractions that have different numerators (top digit) and denominators (bottom digit) but have the same value
Face	a flat surface on a three-dimensional shape
Factor	a number that divides exactly into another number
Formula	a rule for working out unknown values that are represented by words or letters
Highest common factor (HCF)	the highest factor that two or more numbers have in common
Improper fractions	fractions that have larger numerators than denominators
Irregular	a polygon whose sides are not all equal in length and / or whose angles are not all equal in size
Index (or power)	an indication that a number should be multiplied by itself
Indices	the plural of index
Linear sequence	a sequence that ascends (goes up) or descends (goes down) by the same amount with each jump
Lowest common multiple (LCM)	the lowest multiple that two or more numbers have in common
Mean	an average value that gives you an idea of the whole set of values
Mixed numbers	numbers that consist of a whole number and a fraction
Multiples	numbers that can be made by multiplying two numbers together, for example the multiples of 5 are 5, 10, 15, 20 and so on

Negative numbers	numbers that are lower than zero
nth term	an expression for working out any term in a sequence
Order of operations	the order in which you should deal with operations when there is more than one calculation required: **B**rackets, **I**ndices, **D**ivision and **M**ultiplication, **A**ddition and **S**ubtraction
Percentage (%)	values used to show portions of whole amounts by dividing them into 100 equal parts
Perimeter	a measurement of the distance around the outside of a shape
Polygon	any shape with straight sides

Polygon	Number of sides
Triangle	3
Quadrilateral	4
Pentagon	5
Hexagon	6
Heptagon	7
Octagon	8

Positive numbers	numbers that are higher than zero
Prime numbers	numbers that have exactly two factors: 1 and the number itself
Prism	a three-dimensional shape that has the same cross-section throughout its length
Pyramid	a three-dimensional shape with a polygon-shaped base and with triangular faces from the base that all meet at a vertex
Quadrilateral	a shape with 4 straight sides

Quadrilateral	Properties
Kite	2 pairs of adjacent equal sides 1 pair of opposite equal angles
Parallelogram	2 pairs of equal and parallel opposite sides 2 pairs of opposite equal angles
Rhombus	4 equal sides in 2 parallel pairs 2 pairs of opposite equal angles
Trapezium	1 pair of opposite parallel sides

Ratio	the proportion of two or more amounts in integer form, separated by a :
Reflection	the flipping of a shape in a mirror line to produce a mirror image
Regular	a polygon with sides of equal length and angles of equal size

I	V	X	L	C	D	M
1	5	10	50	100	500	1000

Roman numerals a number system first used in Ancient Rome that uses letters to represent numbers

Scale factors numbers used to describe the enlargement of shapes

Square number the result of multiplying a number by itself

Translation the movement of a shape horizontally or vertically, or sometimes both

Triangle a shape with 3 straight sides

Triangle	Properties
Equilateral triangle	3 equal sides and 3 equal angles
Isosceles triangle	2 equal sides and 2 equal angles
Scalene triangle	no equal sides and no equal angles

Vertex a point where three or more edges meet on a three-dimensional shape

Vertices the plural of vertex

Volume a measurement of the space covered by a three-dimensional shape

Useful formulae

- Area of a rectangle (or square) = length × width
- Area of a parallelogram (or rhombus) = base × height
- Area of a triangle = $\frac{1}{2}$ base × height
- Volume of a cuboid (or cube) = length × width × height
- Mean average = total of the values ÷ number of values
- Diameter = 2 × radius
- 1.6 kilometres (km) ≈ 1 mile
- 4.5 litres (l) ≈ 1 gallon
- 1 kilogram (kg) ≈ 2.2 pounds (lb)
- 2.5 centimetres (cm) ≈ 1 inch (in)

Notes

Answers

Number

1 Ordering and rounding numbers

1 (50 000) — The 5 is in the 10 000 column of a place value grid.

2 (43 221)

3 **a** 861 600

    b 860 000

    c 862 000

    d 861 590

4 1677 — The smallest number is in the thousands column and the next smallest number is in the hundreds column, so this is the smallest number possible.

5 **a** (March)

    b April

    c 15 100 m — You need to round the 50 up to the nearest 100

2 Negative numbers

1 −7 — The sequence increases in jumps of 4 each time.

2 **a** (−5 °C)

    b 07.00

    c 13 °C

3 (B)

4 **a** −7, −5, −2, +1, +3, +4

    b Round 5

a Read up from 08.00 on the x-axis to the graph line. Then read across to −5 °C on the y-axis.
b Read across from −6 °C on the y-axis, then read down to half-way between 06.00 and 08.00 on the x-axis.
c The temperature at 06.00 was −7 °C. The temperature at 12.00 was 6 °C. Count on from −7 to 6 to find the difference of 13.

3 Decimal numbers

1 7.064, 6.704, 6.407, 6.074, 6.047

2 (9.09)

3 9.512 → 10

    0.098 → 0

    9.053 → 9

    0.801 → 1

4 **a** Flour: 1.3 kg

    b Butter 0.6 kg

    c Sugar: 0.3 kg

    d Raisins: 0.2 kg

5 **a** 9.86 s, 9.79 s; 9.69 s; 9.58 s — The slowest time is the largest number. The fastest time is the smallest number.

    b 2009

    c (no) — Maurice Green's time rounds up from 9.79 s to 9.8 s. Ato Bolden's time rounds up from 9.86 s to 9.9 s

Calculation

4 Mental addition and subtraction

1 (4299) •————————————————————

2 CXXXVIII •————

3 10 000 − 9648 = 352 words •————

4 a 850 ml

   b 725 ml

5 1000

6 a (− 51); 259

   b (+ 210); 10 331

> Round 4201 to 4200 and take this away from 8500 to get 4300. 4300 − 1 = 4299

> Hadrian was born in 76 AD. 76 + 62 = 138 AD

> Use chunking to count on from 9648 to find the difference.

5 Column addition and subtraction

1 7412 •————————————————————

2 6044 •————

3 a £4.47 •————

   b £23.49

   c £1.88 •————

4 a 6511

   b 608

   c (12 143) •————

5 37 250 l

6 £2410

> Add the numbers together to find the total.

> You need to borrow from the hundreds column.

> To find the profit subtract the cost (£6.68) from the price (£11.15) using column subtraction.

> Find the difference by subtracting the lower cost from the higher cost.

> Use column addition to add up the numbers for each year.

6 Multiplication

1 (9840) •————————————————————

2 a 0.2

   b 0.073

   c 1.5

   d 8

3 7416

4 1353 •————

5 3576 km

6 (0.01 × 400)

7 a £80.82

   b £260.96 •————

   c £618.80

   d £130.64

> Work out the answer by reversing the calculation: $9.84 \times 100 = 9840$

> Use long multiplication to find the product of two two-digit numbers.

> a £4.49 × 18 = £80.82
> Make sure you keep the decimal point in the same column when using long multiplication.
> b £9.32 × 28 = £260.96
> c The shop sells 70 calculators in February, so £8.84 × 70 = £618.80
> d The shop sells 23 pencil cases in February, so £5.68 × 23 = £130.64

7 Division

1 **a** 100

   b 10

   c 1000

2 (7.25)

3 116

4 (5.7)

5 **a** 143

   b 11.5

   c 5

6 (15)

7 28 cm

8 **a** £7.50

   b £17.68

   c 21 people

> $58 \div 8 = 7 \text{ r } 2; 7 \text{ r } 2 = 7\frac{2}{8}; 7\frac{2}{8} = 7\frac{1}{4}; 7\frac{1}{4} = 7.25$

> Use short division to divide by a single-digit number.

> $5.7 \times 10 = 57; 57 \times 100 = 5700$

> **a** $13 \times 11 = 143$
> **b** $69 \div 6 = 11 \text{ r } 3; 11 \text{ r } 3 = 11\frac{3}{6}; 11\frac{3}{6} = 11.5$
> **c** $20 \div 5 = 4$, so $2 \div 5 = 0.4$

> $129 \div 9 = 14 \text{ r } 3$. The remainder means that the fossils will not all fit into 14 cases, so Amir needs 15 cases.

Fractions, decimals & percentages

8 Fractions

1 **a** $\left(\frac{4}{10}\right)$

   b $\frac{2}{5}$

2 $\frac{1}{6}, \frac{4}{9}, \frac{3}{6}, \frac{6}{9}, \frac{11}{12}$

3 $\frac{10}{16}, \frac{25}{40}, \frac{20}{32}$

4 **a** $\left(2\frac{1}{6}\right)$

   b $\left(\frac{13}{3}\right)$

5 **a** $\frac{3}{9}$

   b $\frac{4}{5}$

   c (yes)

> Divide the numerator and denominator by 2

> Work out how much either the numerator or denominator has been multiplied by, and multiply the other number by the same amount.

> **a** Use the largest number as the denominator and the smallest number as the numerator.
> **b** A proper fraction is between 0 and 1. The largest proper fraction will be as close to 1 as possible.
> **c** The largest improper fraction will have the largest number as the numerator and the smallest number as the denominator: $\frac{9}{3} = 3$

9 Percentages

1 (12)

2 44%

3 60%

4 (30 g)

5 **a** 48%

   b 40 people

   c (yes)

> 10% of 30 = 3; 4 × 3 = 12.

> 11 of the 25 squares on the grid are shaded. $\frac{11}{25}$ is equivalent to $\frac{44}{100}$, which is 44%

> If 70% = 21 g, then 10% = 21 g ÷ 7 = 3 g; 10 × 3 g = 30 g

10 Equivalence

1 $10\% \rightarrow \frac{1}{10}$; $\frac{1}{4} \rightarrow 25\%$; $\frac{2}{5} \rightarrow 0.4$; $0.6 \rightarrow \frac{3}{5}$ •————————

Convert all the numbers to fractions.

2 $\frac{37}{50}$, 75%, 0.76, $\frac{78}{100}$

3 a 20%

   b 0.4 •————————

a One of the five sectors is shaded. $\frac{1}{5} = 20\%$

b Two of the five sectors are unshaded.
$\frac{2}{5} = 40\% = 0.4$

4 a 50%

   b $\frac{1}{3}$

Ratio and proportion

11 Ratio and proportion

1 (2:3)

2 36 strawberries

3 a 40 cards

   b 72 cards

a 225 ÷ 75 = 3, so Lucy uses 3 times more butter.
Therefore, 500 × 3 = 1500 g
b Lucy needs 3 times more sugar. 150 × 3 = 450 g,
not 425 g

4 a (1500 g) •————————

   b (no)

5 a 1:3

a An octagonal room has 8 walls. 2 walls are green,
so 6 must be white. Simplify the ratio 2:6 using
the common factor of 2 to find the ratio 1:3
b 6 of the walls are white, so 3 must be painted
yellow. Therefore, there are 3 yellow walls and 5 of
other colours.

   b 3:5 •————————

12 Scale factors

1 (60 cm) •————————

5 cm × 3 = 15 cm; 15 cm × 4 = 60 cm

2 a

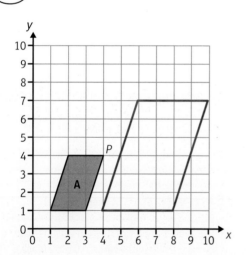

   b (10, 7)

3 a 64 km² •————————

   b (16 km²)

a The sides of the new housing development are
the same length as the sides of the town.
8 km × 8 km = 64 km²
b Enlarging by a scale factor of 0.5 means
halving the lengths of the sides of the new
housing development. 8 km ÷ 2 = 4 km so
4 km × 4 km = 16 km²

4 a (6 cm)

   b (no)

   c 2.5 cm

Shape and measurement

13 Converting units

1 92 g, 0.92 kg, 92 000 g, 920 kg

> Convert all the numbers to kg. 92 g = 0.092 kg and 92 000 g = 92 kg

2 200 cm → 2 m; 200 mm → 0.2 m;

20 m → 2000 cm; 2 cm → 20 mm

3 **a** 4800 ml

b 1100 ml

> **a** 4.8 l × 1000 = 4800 ml
> **b** 2.5 l – 1.4 l = 1.1 l; 1.1 l × 1000 = 1100 ml
> **c** 4.8 l + 2.5 l + 1.4 l = 8.7 l. To get an approximate answer, round 8.7 l to 9 l and divide by 4.5 l, because there are 4.5 l in 1 gal.

c (2 gal)

4 (800 km)

> 1.6 has been rounded to 1.5 for the approximation: 1200 ÷ 1.5 = 800 miles

5 1750 hours

14 Perimeter

1 (16 cm)

> Count around the outside of the shape.

2 32 m

> The missing measurements are 9 m – 3 m = 6 m and 7 m – 5 m = 2 m.

3 **a** A

b 2 m

> Pool A is 11 m + 11 m + 4 m + 4 m = 30 m.
> Pool B is 9 m + 9 m + 5 m + 5 m = 28 m.

4 **a** (8.4 m)

b (yes)

5 **a** 720 cm

> Total the perimeter in centimetres
> (12 × 50 cm + 8 × 30 cm = 840 cm) then divide by 100 to convert to metres.

b y = 60 cm

6 (500 m)

15 Area

1 (1.21 m^2)

2 12 cm^2

3 147 m^2

4 (625 cm^2)

> The perimeter of 100 cm divided into four equal length sides = 100 cm ÷ 4 = 25 cm. Use column multiplication to find the area:
> 25 cm × 25 cm = 625 cm^2

5 **a** 6 m

b 2 m

c the lawn

d 38 m^2

> **a** 10 m – 4 m = 6 m
> **b** 5 m – 3 m = 2 m
> **c** Area of the lawn = 5 m × 4 m = 20 m^2; area of the patio = 3 m × 6 m = 18 m^2
> **d** 20 m^2 + 18 m^2 = 38 m^2
> **e** The area of the existing lawn is 20 m^2; the patio is now 3 m × 3 m = 9 m^2, so there is another 3 m by 3 m area of lawn. 20 m^2 + 9 m^2 = 29 m^2

e 29 m^2

16 Reflections and translations

1 **a** (−5, −4)

> The x and y coordinates are both negative.

b B (−4, 8); D (4, 0)

2

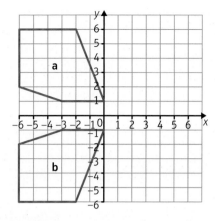

3 **a** (false)

   b (true)

   c (false)

   d (true)

> **a** Point *E* sits at 60 along the *x*-axis and 50 up the *y*-axis, therefore the coordinates are (60, 50) not (50, 60).
> **c** The coordinates of *F* would be (−10, −20).
> **d** Point *F* is (10, −20). When it is reflected in the *x*-axis, the *y*-coordinate becomes positive (10, 20).

4 **a** (isosceles)

   b (0, 12)

   c (down 1 and left 4)

   d (−9, 2)

> **a** The triangle has a flat base between points *B* and *C*. The top of the triangle is (7, 10), which is halfway between the other two corners.
> **b** Point *A* is (7, 10). Subtract 7 from the *x*-coordinate and add 2 to the *y*-coordinate to work out the new position of point *A*.
> **c** To translate the coordinates to the new position, subtract:
> 5 − 4 = 1; 2 − 1 = 1; (5, 2) → down 1; left 4 → (1, 1).
> **d** The *x*-coordinate will be negative, but the *y*-coordinate will stay the same.

Calculation

17 Estimating

1 **a** 8200

   b 150 000

   c 100

   d 7000

2 **a** no

   b (31 × 19)

3 **a** £63 000

   b £60 000

   c £260 000

   d Europe and Asia

> **a** £62 500 rounds up to the nearest 1000
> **b** £90 000 − £30 000 = £60 000
> **c** £60 000 + £30 000 + £90 000 + £80 000 = £260 000
> **d** Europe rounds up to £80 000 and Asia rounds down to £60 000; £80 000 + £60 000 = £140 000

18 Multiples and factors

1 (5, 7, 11, 13)

2 25

> The lowest common multiple of 4 and 5 is 20; the highest common factor of 10 and 5 is 5; 20 + 5 = 25

3 (1, 28) (2, 14) (4, 7)

> 3, 5, 6 and 9 are not factors of 28

4

	Factors of 42	Multiples of 3
Multiples of 7	21, 14	84, 21
Factors of 63	21	21, 9

> 21 is a factor of 63 and 42, and a multiple of 3 and 7, so it can go in any box.

5 **A** The lowest common multiple of 6 and 8 is 24

B 5 is a factor of 25, not a multiple.
C 16 is the highest common factor of 32 and 48

6 **a** 99

b 19

a $11 \times 9 = 99$
b The next closest prime number is 17 or 23

19 Order of operations

1 ⟨42⟩

$4^2 = 16; 16 \times 2 = 32; 10 + 32 = 42$

2 $21 \div (3 + 4) \times 6 = 18$

$3 + 4 = 7; 21 \div 7 = 3; 3 \times 6 = 18$

3 **a** ⟨false⟩

b ⟨true⟩

c ⟨false⟩

d ⟨true⟩

a $3 \times 2 = 6; 6^2 = 36; 3^2 = 9$
b $28 \div 7 = 4; 7 + 4 = 11$
c $41 - 11 = 30; 30 + 30 = 60$
d $2 + 1 = 3; 3^3 = 27; 10 \times 27 = 270; 270 \div 3 = 90$

4 $6 + 3 - 5 = 4$

$4 \times 6 - 4^2 = 8$

$5^2 - 6 \times 3 = 7$

$6 \div 4 \times 6 = 9$

5 **a** | < |

b | > |

c | = |

a $6 + (3 \times 9) = 33; (6 + 3) \times 9 = 81$
b $10 \times (2^3 + 2) = 100; (10 \times 2^3) + 2 = 82$
c $30 + 5 \times 4 = 50; 5 \times 4 + 30 = 50$

6 ⟨yes⟩

$2 \times 2 + 2 \times 2 = (2 \times 2) + (2 \times 2) = 8$ and
$2 + 2 \times 2 + 2 = 2 + (2 \times 2) + 2 = 8$

Fractions, decimals & percentages

20 Comparing fractions

1 **a** $\frac{24}{9}$

b $\frac{9}{5}$

c $\frac{16}{6}$

d $\frac{16}{10}$

e a and c

$\frac{8}{3} = \frac{16}{6} = 2\frac{4}{6} = \frac{24}{9}$

2 ⟨$1\frac{1}{4}$⟩

$\frac{10}{8} = \frac{5}{4} = 1\frac{1}{4}$

3 **a** ⟨$\frac{39}{12}$⟩

b ⟨$\frac{32}{5}$⟩

a $3\frac{1}{3} = \frac{10}{3}; \frac{10}{3} = \frac{40}{12}$
b $\frac{32}{5} = \frac{96}{15}$

4 **a** | > |

b | < |

c | = |

a Use a common denominator of 20 to compare.
$\frac{2}{5} = \frac{8}{20}; \frac{1}{4} = \frac{5}{20}$; therefore $\frac{2}{5}$ is larger.
b Convert to improper fractions and use a common denominator of 15 to compare.
$1\frac{3}{5} = \frac{8}{5}; 1\frac{2}{3} = \frac{5}{3}; \frac{8}{5} = \frac{24}{15}; \frac{5}{3} = \frac{25}{15}$;
therefore $1\frac{3}{5}$ is smaller.
c Convert to improper fractions and use a common denominator of 4 to compare. $3\frac{3}{4} = \frac{15}{4}; \frac{30}{8} = \frac{15}{4}$
therefore the fractions are equivalent.

5 **a** $\frac{4}{3}$

b $\frac{10}{15}$

c $\frac{8}{7}$

21 Calculating with fractions

1 $\frac{1}{2}$ —————————————————— $\frac{1}{3} = \frac{2}{6}$; $\frac{5}{6} - \frac{2}{6} = \frac{3}{6}$; $\frac{3}{6} = \frac{1}{2}$

2 **a** >

   b =

   c <

3 **a** 80 ——————————— **a** $\frac{1}{3} \times 240 = 80$

   b 100   **b** $\frac{1}{3} \times 240 = 80$; $\frac{1}{4} \times 240 = 60$; $240 - 80 - 60 = 100$

4 **a** 60

   b $\frac{2}{3}$

   c 30

5 **a** $\frac{5}{4}$

   b 10

Shapes and their properties

22 Areas of other shapes

                        $4.8\,\text{cm} \times 5\,\text{cm} = 24\,\text{cm}^2$

1 (24 cm²) ——————————

2 14 m ——————————— $112\,\text{m}^2 \div 16\,\text{m} = 7\,\text{m}$, so $\frac{1}{2}$ the height is 7 m, making

3 7.5 cm²   the height $7\,\text{m} \times 2 = 14\,\text{m}$

4 (1.5 cm²)
                        Do not halve 6 cm × 5 cm. Apply the scale factor to
5 16.25 cm²   the dimensions first: 6 cm × 0.5 = 3 cm and
                        5 cm × 0.5 = 2.5 cm; 3 cm × 2.5 cm = 7.5 cm²
6 **a** 2.5 m

   b 6 m²   **A** area = 9 cm × (12 cm ÷ 2) = 54 cm²
                        B area = 6 cm × (18.5 cm ÷ 2) = 55.5 cm²
   c 50 tents   55.5 cm² − 54 cm² = 1.5 cm²

23 Volume

1 (11 cm³) ——————————— There are 9 visible cubes and 2 hidden cubes.

2 24 cm³
                        3 lots of 8 cubes each could be added to complete
3 770 000 mm³   the cuboid.

4 5 cm ———————————— 110 mm × 100 mm × 70 mm = 770 000 mm³

5 (8 times)
                        90 cm³ ÷ 3 cm ÷ 6 cm = 5 cm
6 **a** 1500 cm³

   b (500 cm³)

   c 10 cm, 10 cm, 5 cm

   d 800 cakes

24 Square and cube numbers

                        8 × 8 = 64, so 80 × 80 = 6400
1 (6400) ——————————

2 125 ————————————— This is a sequence of cube numbers.

3 **a** 65
                        a 4 × 4 = 16; 7 × 7 = 49; 16 + 49 = 65
   b 116 —————————— **b** 6 × 6 × 6 = 216; 10 × 10 = 100; 216 − 100 = 116
                        c 8 × 8 × 8 = 512; 512 × 2 = 1024
   c 1024

4 64 − 8 = 56 •————————————————————• $4^3 − 2^3 = 56$ is also acceptable.

5 **a** | < |

   b | > | •————————————————————• **a** $5^3 = 5 \times 5 \times 5 = 125$; $122 = 12 \times 12 = 144$; $125 < 144$

   c | = | | **b** $3^3 = 3 \times 3 \times 3 = 27$; $52 = 5 \times 5 = 25$; $27 > 25$
   | **c** $8^2 = 8 \times 8 = 64$; $43 = 4 \times 4 \times 4 = 64$; $64 = 64$

6 7^2, 4^3, 11^2, 5^3, 10^3

25 Triangles and quadrilaterals

1 ⑦ •————————————————————• 4 rotated triangles would fit along the base of the trapezium and 3 triangles would fit between them along the top of the trapezium.

2 78°

3 **a** a kite

   b (no)

4 From top to bottom: trapezium, kite, rhombus

5 **a** 3

   b 4

   c square

6 (−3, 4) and (3, 4) •————————————————————• The x values have stayed the same and the y angles have increased by 7

7 **a** scalene

   b (no) •————————————————————• The shaded shape is a scalene triangle, which has no equal angles.

   c (no) •————————————————————• The shaded shape is smaller in area.

26 Polygons and 3D shapes

1 pentagon → 5; hexagon → 6; heptagon → 7; octagon → 8

2 **a** triangles, hexagons

   b triangles, squares, hexagons

   c triangles, squares

3 cuboid → **D**, triangular prism → **C**, cylinder → **B**, triangle-based pyramid → **A**

4 square-based pyramid •————————————————————• This polygon has 6 sides.

5 (irregular) hexagon •————

6 (irregular) octagon •————————————————————• The overall shape would have 8 sides that are not all the same length.

7 **a** 6

   b 12 •————————————————————• A vertex is another name for a corner. A hexagonal prism has 6 vertices at each end of the prism.

   c 1 •————————————————————• A cone has one edge around the circular base.

27 Angles

1 **a** (false) •————————————————————• Angle a is 140°, so it is an obtuse angle between 90° and 180°

   b (true)

   c (false)

   d (false) •————————————————————• A three-quarter turn is 270°. Angle b is just less than a three-quarter turn, so the closest estimate is 260°

2 (260°) •————

3 96° → obtuse; 330° → reflex; 31° → acute;

180° → straight line

4 a yes

   b no

5 a 130° obtuse

   b 115° obtuse

   c 90° right angle

6 a true

   b false

   c false

> **a** The trapezium Shannon has drawn is irregular. It looks like this:
>
>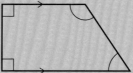
>
> **b** A kite can't have two reflex angles.

> **a** The sum of the angles inside a triangle is 180° and reflex angles are greater than 180°
> **b** A right angle is 90°
> **c** Obtuse angles are greater than 90°

28 Angle properties

1 a angle c

   b angle b

   c 45°

> **a** 270° − 235° = 35°
> **b** 180° − 125° = 55°
> **c** 90° − 45° = 45°

2 360°

> The internal angles of a quadrilateral always add up to 360°

3 a true

   b true

   c false

   d true

> **b** Angle y is vertically opposite the known angle, and the angles are around a straight line, so it must also be 138°
> **c** 180° − 138° = 42°
> **d** $z = 360 − (138° + 42° + 138°) = 360 − 318 = 42°$; therefore $z = x$

4 a 40°

   b 70°

5 44°

6 50°

> **a** The interior angles of a triangle add up to 180°
> 180° − 110° − 30° = 40°
> **b** The angles on a straight line add up to 180°
> 180° − 110° = 70°

7 a 30°

   b 90°

   c 120°

Algebra

29 Equations and formulae

1 $x \div 20$

> The total price of x pence is divided by the number of slices to find the cost per slice.

2 a $2a + b + 2c = 21$

   b $b = 3$ and $c = 4$

3 $d = 12$

4 $z = 3$

5 $P = 6w$

6 $x = -4$

> $2a + b + 2c = 21$; $10 + b + 2c = 21$; $b + 2c = 21 − 10$; $b + 2c = 11$; $3 + (2 \times 4) = 11$

> $3d \div 4 = 9$; $3d = 9 \times 4 = 36$; $d = 36 \div 3$; so $d = 12$

30 Linear sequences

1 **a** (6, 10, 14, 18, 22…)

    b ($4n + 2$)

> **a** This is the only sequence where the numbers change by the same value (+4) each time.
> **b** The first term = $(4 × 1) + 2 = 6$; the second term = $(4 × 2) + 2 = 10$, etc.

2 **a** (true)

    b (false)

    c (true)

> **a** This sequence of numbers ascends by the same value (+9) each time.
> **b** $15 + 9 = 24$
> **c** The first term = $9 × 1 − 3 = 6$; the second term = $9 × 2 − 3 = 15$, etc.

3 **a** 14, 38

    b 86

> **a** $(8 × 2) − 2 = 14$ and $(8 × 5) − 2 = 38$
> **b** $(8 × 11) − 2 = 86$

4 96, 87, 78

5 −1

6 (120)

Statistics

31 Tables, charts and graphs

1 **a** (100)

    b $\frac{1}{8}$

    c (37.5%)

    d (false); (true); (false)

> **a** $\frac{1}{4}$ of 400 children visited Italy = 100 children.
> **b** The children who went to France take up one of the eight sectors of the pie chart.
> **c** Work out $\frac{3}{8}$ as a percentage. $\frac{1}{4}$ = 25%, so $\frac{1}{8}$ = 12.5%; 12.5% × 3 = 37.5%
> **d** The same number of children went to Italy as Turkey.
> $\frac{3}{8}$ of the children went to Portugal. $\frac{3}{8}$ of 400 is 150
> 50 children went to France and 250 went to Italy or Portugal, so five times as many went.

2 **a** (3 h 59 min)

    b 11.17

    c 16.07

3 **a** 2

    b 3 hours

    c (10 km per hour)

    d 11.30 and 12.00

> **a** The horizontal sections on the graph show where Lenny stopped – at 11.00 and 12.00
> **b** Lenny started his journey at 10.00 and finished at 13.00, making a total time of 3 hours (including his breaks).
> **c** He travelled 10 km in the first hour of his journey.
> **d** The steepest part of the graph shows where Lenny travelled fastest. He travelled 20 km in this half an hour.

32 Mean average

1 0.9 or $\frac{9}{10}$

> Convert the fractions to decimals first. 1.5 + 0.5 + 1.75 + 0.25 + 0.5 = 4.5; 45 ÷ 5 = 9, so 4.5 ÷ 9 = 0.9

2 **a** (£22)

    b £7

    c £3 per month

    d £31

> **a** £21 + £35 + £14 + £11 + £30 + £21 = £132; £132 ÷ 6 = £22
> **b** Use algebra to find the missing data for June: £12 + £30 + £27 + £13 + £19 = £101; $(x + £101) ÷ 6 = £18$; $x + £101 = £18 × 6$; $x + £101 = £108$; $x = £108 − £101$; $x = £7$
> **c** Jonny spent £18 per month in the first half of the year. In the second half, his average spending was £21 per month. £21 − £18 = £3
> **d** £19 + £25 = £44; $(x + £44) ÷ 3 = £25$; $x + £44 = £25 × 3$; $x + £44 = £75$; $x = £75 − £44$; $x = £31$

3 (55 km per hour)

4 9, 2, 8

5 40p

> 80 + 30 = 110; 110 ÷ 2 = 55 km per hour.

> 9 + 2 + 8 = 19. This is the highest total possible.

> Gemma buys 20 pens for £8.00; £8.00 ÷ 20 = 800p ÷ 20 = 40p per pen.

Published by Pearson Education Limited, 80 Strand, London, WC2R 0RL.

www.pearsonschools.co.uk

Text © Pearson Education Limited 2018
Edited, typeset and produced by Elektra Media Ltd
Original illustrations © Pearson Education Limited
Illustrated by Elektra Media Ltd
Cover design by Lukas Bischoff

The right of Giles Clare to be identified as author of this work has been asserted by him in accordance with the Copyright, Designs and Patents Act 1988.

First published 2018

21 20 19 18
10 9 8 7 6 5 4 3 2 1

British Library Cataloguing in Publication Data
A catalogue record for this book is available from the British Library

ISBN: 978 1 292 24669 7

Printed in Slovakia by Neografia

Acknowledgements

We would like to thank Amanda Booth for her invaluable help in the development and trialling of this publication.

Note from the publisher
Pearson has robust editorial processes, including answer and fact checks, to ensure the accuracy of the content in this publication, and every effort is made to ensure this publication is free of errors. We are, however, only human, and occasionally errors do occur. Pearson is not liable for any misunderstandings that arise as a result of errors in this publication, but it is our priority to ensure that the content is accurate. If you spot an error, please do contact us at resourcescorrections@pearson.com so we can make sure it is corrected.